THIS BOOK

...Harry..(Scoo...

THE WORLD'S MOST ADORABLE/VILE/
ATTRACTIVE/STUPID/CUTE/AWFUL/
SMELLY/BEAUTIFUL/CAPRICORNIAN

WITH KIND REGARDS/ALL MY LOVE
~~YOURS IN DISGUST~~ ...Fiona..,..Ian.,..Tanya....

P.S. PLEASE TAKE NOTE OF PAGE(S)
7.,.9,.11,..14, 28, 54..................

THE CAPRICORN BOOK

A CORGI BOOK 0 552 12313 7

First publication in Great Britain
PRINTING HISTORY
Corgi edition published 1983

Corgi Books are published by Transworld Publishers Ltd.,
Century House, 61-63 Uxbridge Road, Ealing, London W5 5SA

Made and printed in Great Britain by the
Guernsey Press Co. Ltd., Guernsey, Channel Islands.

THE CAPRICORN BOOK

BY IAN HEATH

CAPRICORN
DECEMBER 21 - JANUARY 19

TENTH SIGN OF THE ZODIAC
SYMBOL : THE GOAT
RULING PLANET : SATURN
COLOURS : BLACK, WHITE, NAVY
GEMS : DARK SAPPHIRE, JADE
NUMBER : EIGHT
DAY : SATURDAY
METAL : LEAD
FLOWER : POPPY

ZZZZZZZZZZ

The CAPRICORN at work................

... INSISTS ON OBEDIENCE ....

....WORKS 'ROUND THE CLOCK.......

......IS LEVEL-HEADED..........

.......HAS A WAY WITH WORDS.......

.........IS ARTISTIC...............

.... DECISIVE ....

.... A GO-GETTER...........

...HAS TO BE IN COMMAND..........

...LIKES CONTACT WITH PUBLIC....

.....AND IS RESPECTED.

.......A MUSICIAN..................

....BOMB-DISPOSAL EXPERT.......

.... ART-DEALER ....

.... STREET-TRADER ....

.... INVISIBLE MENDER..........

......ROOFING CONTRACTOR........

.....OR FRENCH POLISHER.

.....HATES WASHING-UP...............

..... COOKS EXOTIC DISHES..........

.....LIKES COOL SHOWERS..........

.......READS A LOT...............

...SWITCHES ON BREAKFAST T.V........

.. HAS A CRAVING FOR LUXURY........

...WON'T TOLERATE SALESMEN......

......COLLECTS INDOOR PLANTS.....

.... KEEPS PETS ....

.....AND ENJOYS DECORATING.

.........FISH AND CHIPS................

......FEELING SECURE...............

BUBBLE - BATHS

.... FISHING.....................

.......FRIENDLY DISCUSSIONS.........

....AND CHEESECAKE.

The CAPRICORN dislikes ....

..........PEA-SOUP.................

.......UGLY PEOPLE ....

.... PLASTIC FLOWERS..........

.... SMELLY FEET..................

. . . . WINTER . . . .

.....AND SMOKERS.

..... IS VERY POSSESSIVE ....

.......LAUGHS A LOT................

..........IS SHY.....................

.........DETERMINED...................

...LIKES ROMANTIC DINNERS.......

...CAN FLIRT A LITTLE..............

...... IS TERRIBLY JEALOUS..........

..........SOMETIMES PASSIONATE.......

58

.... A LATE DEVELOPER..............

...AND LIKES THE LIGHTS OFF.

CAPRICORN AND PARTNER

HEART RATINGS

♥♥♥♥♥ WOWEE !!
♥♥♥♥ GREAT, BUT NOT 'IT'
♥♥♥ O.K. — COULD BE FUN
♥♥ FORGET IT
♥ RUN THE OTHER WAY — FAST!

TAURUS VIRGO

AQUARIUS SAGITTARIUS
PISCES SCORPIO

ARIES CANCER CAPRICORN

LIBRA GEMINI

LEO

CAPRICORN PEOPLE

AL CAPONE : ELVIS PRESLEY
RUDYARD KIPLING : OLIVER HARDY
GEORGE BURNS : CARY GRANT
HOWARD HUGHES : JANE FONDA
MARTIN LUTHER KING

JOAN OF ARC : DANNY KAYE
DAVID BOWIE : CHUCK BERRY
J. EDGAR HOOVER : ROD STEWART
LOUIS PASTEUR : AVA GARDNER
FELLINI : ALBERT SCHWEITZER
NOSTRADAMUS : HENRY MILLER
HUMPHREY BOGART : STALIN
DAME REBECCA WEST
EDGAR ALLAN POE : JOHN DENVER
DIANE KEATON : MUHAMMED ALI